A MAD SCRAMBLE

Edited by
Albert B. Feldstein

WARNER BOOKS

A Warner Communications Company

WARNER BOOKS EDITION

Copyright © 1970, 1971 and 1977
by E.C. Publications, Inc.

**Title "MAD" used with permission of its owner,
E.C. Publications, Inc.**

This Warner Books Edition is published by
arrangement with E.C. Publications, Inc.

Designed by Thomas Nozkowski

Warner Books, Inc., 75 Rockefeller Plaza, New York, N.Y. 10019

 A Warner Communications Company

Printed in the United States of America

First Printing: June, 1977

Reissued: November, 1982

10 9 8 7 6 5 4

Can a beautiful Debutante from Nob Hill find happiness living in a Police Station with an ill-tempered but lovable Chief of Detectives, a former Juvenile Delinquent, and a handsome but dull Police Sergeant? For the answer to this and other equally ridiculous questions, join us now for MAD's version of "One Cop's Family", namely

IRONRIDE

ARTIST: ANGELO TORRES

WRITER: LOU SILVERSTONE

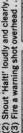

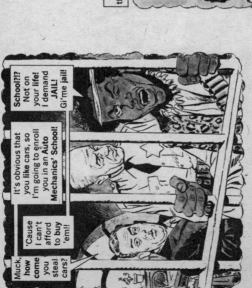

ONE
DAY

AT A
CONSTRUCTION SITE

Nowadays, everything is crooked! Politics is crooked, Real Estate is crooked, Religion is crooked, the TV Repair business is crooked, the Auto Repair business is crooked, etc. Well, we've found one thing that's more crooked than all the rest, and nobody seems to say much about it! So, knowing full well that we may be taking our lives in our hands, the Editors of MAD fearlessly expose.. *Crooked Teeth*... with

THE MAD ORTHODONTIA PRIMER

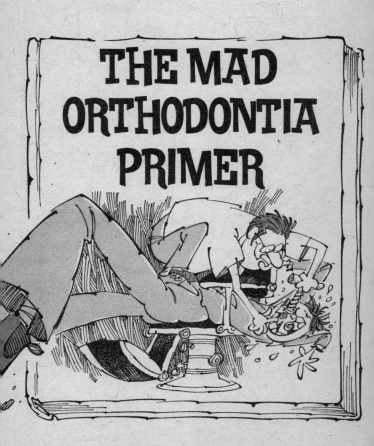

ARTIST: PAUL COKER, JR.

WRITER: LARRY SIEGEL

Chapter 1

See the man.
He is a Dentist.
But he is not a regular Dentist.
He is a special kind of Dentist.
He straightens teeth.
He is called an "Orthodontist."
What is the difference between an
   Orthodontist and a regular Dentist?
Oh . . . about $25,000 a year!

Chapter 2

See the boy.
See the funny way his teeth stick out of his mouth.
His parents have brought him to the Orthodontist
To see if anything can be done.
The Orthodontist has a name for this condition.
He tells the parents he has found a "malocclusion."
The Orthodontist has another name for this condition.
He tells himself he has found a "gold mine."

Chapter 3

See the parents.
They are very uncertain.
They do not know if they want to spend a fortune
    to have the boy's teeth straightened.
But the Orthodontist is very helpful.
"Can you picture your son as a teenager?" he asks.
The parents picture their son as a teenager.

They see him in faded torn jeans and a dirty undershirt.
They see him with long, wild hair hanging over his face.
They see his face covered with pimples.
"Yes, we can picture our son as a teenager," they say.
"Now . . . why should we have his teeth straightened?"
"Because if you don't," says the Orthodontist,
"He will grow up to be ugly!"

Chapter 4

See the boy's mouth.
He is wearing a brace.
What does a brace do?
It straightens teeth.
It also traps food.
The boy will wear the brace for two years.
Tonight, he will eat a sandwich.
The boy will also wear peanut butter for two years.

Chapter 5

See the boy.
What is he wearing now?
It is called a "night brace."
It fits over two wire hooks
Over two wire coils
Over his regular wire brace.
The boy's parents are going out for the evening.
They are leaving him two emergency telephone numbers.
The family doctor . . .
And the family electrician.

Chapter 6

See the neighborhood kids.
All the neighborhood kids wear braces.
The brace is a status symbol.
It is very "in."
See the one little girl cry.
She is crying because her teeth are straight.
She does not need to wear braces.
Cheer up, little girl.
Your teeth may be straight,
But your eyes are crooked!
Perhaps you will soon wear mod, wire-framed Granny glasses.
The Good Lord willing.

Chapter 7

The two years are up.
See the boy's teeth now.
They are all straight.
See the boy and his family walking to the Orthodontist
For the last time.
The Orthodontist will take off the boy's brace.
Why is the family walking to the Orthodontist?
Why don't they ride in the father's nice Buick?
Because the father doesn't have his nice Buick anymore.
He had to sell it to pay for the boy's braces.

Chapter 8

See the Orthodontist.
He is removing the boy's brace.
The boy will never have to wear a brace again.
Ever.
The boy is happy.
The boy's family is happy.
Poor, but happy.
However . . .
To make sure his teeth remain straight,
The Orthodontist announces
That the boy will have to wear a retainer.

Chapter 9

See the retainer.
The retainer is another kind of brace.
The boy will have to wear it for six years
To insure the permanent effect of the first brace.
Isn't that nice?
Of course, there will be a slight charge for the retainer . . .
Plus for each visit over the next six years.
Isn't *that* nice?
In one minute, the Orthodontist will have crooked teeth.
He will call it a "malocclusion."
The boy's father will call it "a punch in the mouth."

THE
LIGHTER
SIDE OF...
BABY

SITTING

ARTIST & WRITER: DAVE BERG

And in case of a **REALLY BIG EMERGENCY,** this is my Hospital's telephone number!

ROGER KAPUTNIK
936 2519

MARVIN COLAYSS
326 9283

DR. MIKE
GUZAUSKI
325 8836

EL HOSPITAL
234 7642

In case you need a baby sitter that doesn't **SCARE** easy, this is my **Big Sister's** telephone number!!

Excuse me, Sir . . . can you tell me where **number "56"** is?

Are you looking for the **Freeman** house?

Yeah! **That's** the place!

It's the third house down from the next corner on the right!

It's a fieldstone house with a large weeping willow out in front! You **can't miss it!**

Thank you, Sir . . .

AND WHEN YOU GET THERE, YOU CAN TELL SUE KELLY WE MADE IT QUITE CLEAR WE DON'T WANT HER BOY-FRIENDS OVER WHEN SHE'S BABY SITTING FOR US!!

Hey! Where's my little girl?

Your "little" girl is now a "big" girl! Tonight, she's on her first job as a baby sitter!

My little girl— a baby sitter!? Why, just a little while ago, we were hiring baby sitters for her!

Then, there was that terrible in-between period when she resented having a sitter and we sat home!

Love Diane

Gee, do you know what this means?! We're free to go out tonight!!

Not exactly!

She calls here every fifteen minutes . . . asking what to do!

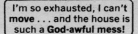

Look at that! My little Naomi has her **first baby sitting job!** She's grown up at last! Now, I can **relax** and **enjoy** my leisure time with no **children** around to **worry** about!

Naomi! Naomi!! The Doyles have invited us on their **cruiser!** Let's go . . .

I can't! I'm baby sitting!

But this is **one chance** in a million!!

Mama . . . what'll I do?!?

While you were out, **Mrs. Ginko** called and asked if you could **baby sit** for them on Saturday night!

I wouldn't work for **them** if theirs was the **last** baby sitting job in the **world!!**

You mean because they have **four bratty hard-to-handle kids?**

Nahhh! I can **cope** with **that!** It's something **worse!**

You mean because they live in a **scary out-of-the-way place?**

Nahhh! I can cope with **that, too!** It's something even **worse!**

They don't have a **color television set!** THAT, I simply **cannot** cope with!

I'm glad you called me **back**, Amy! Sorry I had to **hang up** on you so suddenly, but I thought I heard **Mrs. Barton** at the door! The one thing she **really hates** is to come home and catch me **on the phone!**

I mean, **so what** if I make a few phone calls while I'm baby sitting for her!? Okay, so I **spend** the whole night on the phone! I mean, what's the **big problem**, anyway?!

This is **Mrs. Barton** . . . and the **big problem** is, I can't call and check to see how my **children** are when the line is constantly busy!!

Truthfully, I really **hate** to baby sit! I'm actually terrorized!

I know what you **mean!** There are all the things that go **bump** in the **night**, like **creaky floors** . . .

. . . and **rattling windows** and **groaning air conditioners** and **squeaky heating systems** and **doorbells** that ring and you're afraid to **answer** . . .

David Berg

. . . and **strange noises** and **obscene telephone calls!** Boy, are those things ever terrorizing!

I'm not **talking** about those things! What **REALLY** terrorizes me is **THE KIDS!!**

ON THE "HUNCHBACK OF NOTRE DAME" SET

Let us now glorify the world of sweat-socks and charlie-horses, of third-base slides and 50-yard bombs, of double headers, daily doubles, and double dribbles. Let us thrill to the roar of the crowd and the smell of the locker-room. In other words, let us introduce the following article, mainly . . .

A SPORTS FAN'S GARDEN OF VERSES

ARTIST: JACK DAVIS   WRITER: FRANK JACOBS

THE SPORTSMAN'S HOUR

Between the dusk and the evening,
When the viewing is starting to sour,
Comes a tedious ABC program
That is known as the Sportsman's Hour.

I see on the Zenith before me,
In forests and valleys and lakes,
Celebrities hunting and fishing
Twixt eighteen commercial breaks.

Jim Nabors is gunning for penguin;
Jack Lemmon is clubbing a snail;
And out in the woods Ernest Borgnine
Is having it out with a quail.

Rod Taylor is shooting a marmot;
Dean Martin can't focus to aim;
And off in Iraq Fred MacMurray
Is stalking a hamster that's lame.

Chuck Connors is punching a herring;
Al Hirt is repelling a goose;
And in the Canadian Rockies
Curt Gowdy is boring a moose;

Despite all the shooting and killing,
It gives me great comfort to know
That though all the creatures get slaughtered,
They don't have to watch the show.

THE HOMETOWN GOALIE

Under the spreading hockey net
   The hometown goalie squats;
His brow is creased with purple welts
   From taking head-high shots,
And his battered ears remind us of
   A Boy Scout's granny knots.

          A row of scars conceal a face
             That sparkled once with youth,
          And as he squats he contemplates
             The ever-present truth,
          That soon some puck may extricate
             His one remaining tooth.

SKIS

I think that I have come to see
The reason why most people ski;
It's not the snow upon the hills;
It's not the turns, the jumps, the spills;
It's not the riding in the lift;
It's not collapsing in a drift;
The skiing bit is just a dodge
For making out inside the lodge.

One eye is blue and crossed and glazed,
    The other reddish plaid;
And though his nose is flattened out,
    You'll never see him sad;
He knows that for a first-year man
    He doesn't look too bad.

BROADWAY JOE

You can talk about your guards
An' your fullbacks gainin' yards,
An' your ends who run the hook and down-n-out;
But when it comes to glory
Then your quarterback's the story,
For it's him the fans all want to read about.

Now there's Kapp an' Johnny U.,
An' Bart Starr an' Dawson, too,
An' Fran Tarkenton, who scrambles for his dough;
But of those who pass the ball,
The coolest one of all
Is the hero of the Jet team, Broadway Joe.

For it's Joe, Joe, Joe!
You always make good copy, Broadway Joe!
All the writers are adorin'
How you lead the team in scorin'
An' we don't mean playin' football, Broadway Joe!

Well, he had himself a spree
Greetin' folks at Bach'lors Three,
Lookin' fancy with his Fu Manchu moustache;
Then that feller, Pete Rozelle, he
Said the atmosphere was smelly,
So poor Joe he sold it for a ton of cash.

It's enough to drive ya dizzy
With the way he's keepin' busy
With his "Eatin' Chains" an' "Agencies" an' all;
When some deal he's not financin',
Then he's off somewhere romancin',
An' ya wonder how there's time for playin' ball.

For it's Joe, Joe, Joe!
A blonde is wavin' in the seventh row!
Soon the grandstand will be shakin'
From the passes you'll be makin'
An' we don't mean playin' football, Broadway Joe!

ON THE ROAD TO BALTIMORE

Down the old New Jersey Turnpike
    past the booth that takes the tolls,
There's a baseball team a'playin'
    that they call the Or-i-oles;
For the Birds have lost the Big One,
    like the mighty Colts before;
An' it always seems to happen
    When you play for Baltimore!

COME BOWL WITH ME

Come bowl with me this evening, dear,
And we will kill twelve cans of beer;
We'll join the others on the team
And eat three quarts of peach ice cream,
And in between each frame we bowl
We'll have a burger on a roll,
A dozen hot-dogs, sacks of fries,
A meatball and two apple pies;
Come bowl with me, you really should—
The exercise will do us good!

When you play for Baltimore,
There's an awful fate in store!
Can't you hear the champagne poppin'
    ev-ry place but Baltimore!
On the road to Baltimore
Where the teams lose more an' more,
It's no wonder it's the town
    that all the New York fans adore!

LEW ALCINDOR

In the city of Milwaukee,
Down the highway from Sheboygan,
Dwelt the longest drink of water,
And his name was Lew Alcindor,
And he played the post of center
For the pro team called the Bucks there,
Who were formerly quite lousy,
Being filled with second-raters;
And he dwarfed the other players
Did the long one Lew Alcindor,
For he towered far above them,
Standing taller than the elm tree,
Standing taller than the redwood,
Even taller than the giant
Known as Chamberlain the Laker;
And the long one Lew Alcindor
Learned to stuff the two-point basket,
Learned to grab the tricky rebound,
Learned to jostle in the pivot,
Learned to elbow Knicks and Celtics
When the referees weren't looking;
But the one thing he was learning,
Which impressed the other players,
Yes, the one thing he was learning,
More important than the stuff-shot,
More important than the rebound,
More important that the pivot,
Was the way to sign a contract
For a nifty million dollars.

DOUBLEDAY

In Cooperstown did Doubleday
The game of baseball once create;
In pastures did the fielders play
With splintered bats and balls like clay
   And pie-tins for home plate.

The early game was quite a thrill,
Which made the local fans agree
That though the players might lack skill
And second base was on a hill,
   The game was fun to see.

The game has changed from days of yore,
With sliders flying past each bat,
With players hitting .204,
And fifteen innings with no score,
  And dreadful things like that.

And now, much to the fans' dismay,
An unearned run's a big attack;
 Which makes me sure if Doubleday
Could see this boring game they play,
  He'd take the whole thing back.

I MUST GO OUT TO THE TRACK AGAIN

I must go out to the track again
    to where the bangtails run;
And all I ask is a horse with class
    that goes off at 4 to 1;
And a Racing Form and a green tip sheet
    to help me with my picks;
And my buddy Jerome who'll get the word
    in case there is a fix.

I must go out to the track again
    in time for the Second Race;
And we'll lay fifty bills on Typhoon to win
    and a like amount to place;
And the curses we'll yell when Typhoon runs last,
    for his race does not delight us;
How could we know that in the stretch
    he'd come down with arthritis?

ON A STREETCORNER DOWNTOWN

Several issues back, we ran an article comparing College life in the '40's with life on the Campus today. Since this article received an overwhelming response of utter silence from our readers, we've decided to try again . . . this time by showing the changes that have taken place with respect to the teenagers of the '40's and the teenagers today. So join us now as we take

A MAD LOOK
AT

TWO
HIGH SCHOOL
GENERATIONS

...THEN...
...AND NOW...

ARTIST: PAUL COKER, JR.   WRITER: LOU SILVERSTONE

MOVIES...THEN...

...AND NOW...

CLOTHES...THEN...

...AND NOW...

SMOKING...THEN...

...AND NOW...

WAR...THEN...

...AND NOW...

HAIR...THEN...

...AND NOW...

SCHOOL AUTHORITY...THEN...

...AND NOW...

THE FAMILY CAR...THEN...

...AND NOW...

THE SCHOOL PAPER...THEN...

...AND NOW...

MAD'S

CHRISTMAS

CAROLS

ARTIST: JACK RICKARD
WRITER: FRANK JACOBS

FOR THE
HOLIDAY SEASON

An Eighty-Foot Manger

(Sung to the tune of
"Away In A Manger")

*An eighty-foot manger extends to the street;
With wise men and camels the scene is complete;
A choir of angels is perched on a limb
Beneath a loudspeaker that's blaring a hymn;*

*Our roof features Santa with reindeer and sleigh,
While two dozen floodlights light up the display;
Although it costs thousands, we'd spend even more
Just so we're out-doing our neighbor next door!*

Count The Toll

(Sung to the tune of
"Silver Bells")

Drivers speeding,
Signs unheeding,
Down the highway they race—
You can tell it's the season of Christmas;
Wildly weaving,
Sometimes heaving,
With the cops giving chase—
And with each fatal crack-up you'll hear:

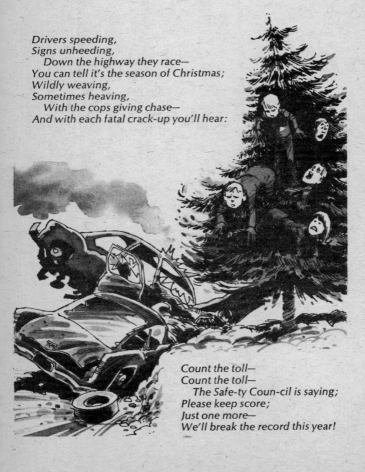

Count the toll—
Count the toll—
The Safe-ty Coun-cil is saying;
Please keep score;
Just one more—
We'll break the record this year!

Hark! The Carol Singers Choke

(Sung to the tune of
"Hark! The Herald Angels Sing!")

Hark! The carol singers cho-ke
From the smog and fumes and smoke;
See them rub their itching e-yes
While the soot pours from the skies;
Filthy air their throats expe-l,
Gasping out "The First No-el;"
Joyful voices cough and hack
While the fresh snow is turning black;
When their final song is sung,
They'll head for home—with one less lung!

God Rest Ye Faithful Football Fans

(Sung to the tune of
"God Rest Ye Merry Gentlemen")

God rest ye faithful football fans,
  This Christmas don't dismay;
Thank God that there's a play-off game
  'Tween Dallas and Green Bay;
The TV tube with all its thrills
  Will hold you for the day—
You won't think . . . of those bills you'll have to pay,
  Bills you must pay—
You won't think of all those bills you'll have to pay!

On New Year's day the bowl games come,
   The Cotton, Orange and Rose;
And then the final championship
   Between the mighty pros;
And all the while you're rooting for
   Your fav'rite team to win,
You'll forget . . . all the bills now pouring in,
   Bills pouring in—
You'll forget the tons of bills now pouring in!

Charlie The Mailman

(Sung to the tune of
"Frosty The Snow Man")

Charlie the mailman
Brings us letters soaked with rain;
Jams our box so full that the mail is crushed,
And then laughs when we complain;

Harry the milkman
Is the biggest slob in town;
Seldom leaves the quarts that we've asked him for;
When he does they're upside down;

Eleven months throughout the year
   they're lousy as can be,
But starting in December they
   show great efficiency—

Then
Charlie and Harry
Really show they're full of zip;
And they'll work that way
Every doggone day
Till they get their Christmas tip!

O Little Town Of Washington

(Sung to the tune of
"O Little Town Of Bethlehem")

O little town of Washington,
We hear no Agnew speech;
 Thy Senate's bare;
 No one is there;
And Nixon's in Palm Beach;

Though Congressmen forsake thee,
We know why they're not here;
 Thy filth and grime
 And slums and crime
Might mar their Christmas cheer!

O little town of Washington,
How still we see thee lie;
   There's not a soul
   Out on a stroll;
Thy crime-rate's gone sky-high;

With rifles and police dogs,
We guard our homes and stores;
   Alive we'll stay
   This Christmas Day
If we don't go out-doors;

Good King Wenceslas

(Sung to the tune of
the popular carol of that name, stupid!)

Good King Wen-ces-las came back
   To the earth this sea-son;
Saw five million lacking food;
   Asked what was the rea-son;
"Do not worry," he was told,
   "If there's some starvation;
"That's our way of holding down
   "Over-popula-a-tion!"

Good King Wen-ces-las then went
   To a field of bat-tle;
Saw a hundred people there,
   Being killed like cat-tle;
"War is helpful," he was told,
   From the field of rub-ble;
"We have found that Army life
   "Keeps boys out of tro-u-ble!"

Good King Wen-ces-las moved on,
    Spied a tanker leak-ing;
Saw the ocean turning black;
    Heard an oil-man speak-ing:
"Unemployment rates will drop,
    "If the spill should reach us—
"There'll be jobs for everyone
    "Cleaning up the be-ea-ches!"

Good King Wen-ces-las turned off
    From the whole routine here;
Went back up to Heaven's Gates,
    Told God what he'd seen here:
"Earth is such an awful place,
    "Only fit for slum-ming—
"If You're smart, You'll drop all plans
    "For the Second C-o-ming!"

Our Plane We Boarded Last Evening, Dear

(Sung to the tune of
"It Came Upon A Midnight Clear")

Our plane we boarded last evening, dear,
To start on our holiday spree;
We read three books and enjoyed our meal,
And saw a movie for free;
We pushed our seats back and slept till dawn,
Then chatted together past noon;
It's been a pleasure, and now let's hope
That we'll be taking off soon!

O Telephone! O Telephone!

(Sung to the tune of
"O Christmas Tree! Fair Christmas Tree!")

O telephone! O telephone!
At Christmas time we're singing;
'Cause telephone, O telephone,
Our loved ones you are ringing;
We call Aunt Sue in Portland, Maine,
And get a drug-store in Fort Wayne;
O telephone! O telephone!
Frustration you are bringing;

O telephone! O telephone!
Our call's been mis-directed;
Though, telephone, dear telephone,
You claim that you're perfected;
We know why you work sloppily—
You're owned by a monopoly;
O telephone! O telephone!
We've just been dis-connected!

They're On Strike! They're On Strike! They're On Strike!

(Sung to the tune of
"Let It Snow! Let It Snow! Let It Snow!")

Oh, the weather outside is cru-el,
And the truck-ers won't bring fu-el;
Their pay offer they don't like—
They're on strike! They're on strike! They're on strike!

Our holiday trash is growing,
But the gar-bage-men aren't showing;
Their pension plan they don't like—
They're on strike! They're on strike! They're on strike!

We've a flood that is pretty rough,
From a break in the water main, dear;
If you want a repairman—Tough!
They're staying out till next year!

We're waiting for Santa's visit;
But his sleigh is late—where is it?
Seems his reindeer won't make the hike—
They're on strike! They're on strike! They're on strike!

VERY
EARLY
ONE
MORNING

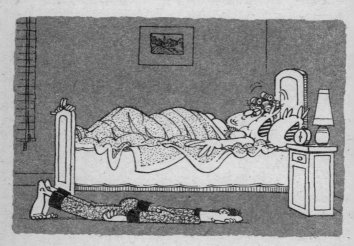

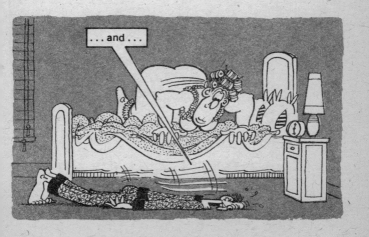

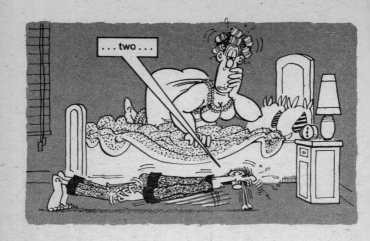

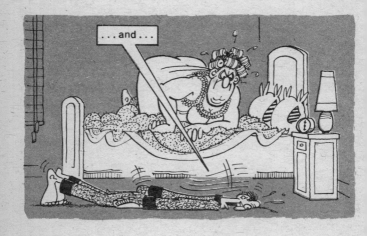

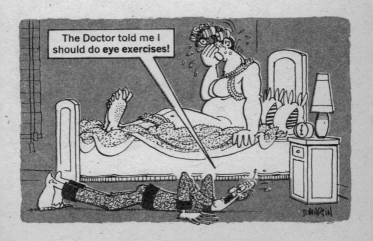

A
MAD
LOOK

LOOK

AT BIRDS

ARTIST & WRITER: SERGIO ARAGONES

Here we go with another MAD "Hate Book" . . . those little gems calculated to make MAD readers feel better by blowing off steam about their pet hates. Since non-smokers are the most intolerant people in the world when it comes to smokers, all of you smokers better skip this article. Because

THE MAD
NON-SM

Don't you hate smokers who...
 . . . put out butts in dishes of food while you're still eating!

it's calculated to make non-smoking MAD readers feel better by blowing off steam about people who, in addition to being addicted to the disgusting habit of smoking, also have disgusting smoking habits. Here, then, Gang, is . . .

OKERS HATE
BOOK

Don't you hate smokers who . . .
. . . smoke while they cook!

ARTIST & WRITER: AL JAFFEE

Don't you hate smokers who . . .
. . . flick their ashes out windows of fast-moving
cars when you're sitting in the rear seat!

Don't you hate smokers who . . .
. . . affect phony smoking poses that are supposed
to make them look smart and sophisticated!

Don't you hate smokers who . . .
. . . bore you with the details of their experiences
every time they attempted to give up smoking!

Don't you hate smokers who . . .
. . . add yet another butt to a full ashtray
without ever once thinking of emptying it!

Don't you hate smokers who . . .
. . . talk without ever removing their cigarette from their mouth!

Don't you hate smokers who . . .
. . . never hit the ashtray no matter how big it is!

Don't you hate smokers who . . .
. . . inflict their particular tastes in nauseating
pipe tobacco aromas on an entire gathering!

Don't you hate smokers who . . .
. . . let their cigarettes burn out in ashtrays,
causing the nearest thing to a tear gas attack!

Don't you hate smokers who . . .
. . . always have tobacco spittle running down their chins!

Don't you hate smokers who . . .
. . . are cutting down on smoking by not carrying any,
but who smoke as much as ever by borrowing!

Don't you hate smokers who . . .
. . . dump ashtrays in toilets!

Don't you hate smokers who . . .
. . . insist upon lighting up while visiting someone
who's in the hospital with a respiratory illness!

Don't you hate smokers who . . .
. . . do tricks with lighted cigarettes!

Don't you hate smokers who . . .
. . . stupidly lean into plastic screens!

Don't you hate smokers who . . .
. . . throw butts that are still alive in wastebaskets!

Don't you hate smokers who . . .
. . . flick cigarette butts out windows!

Don't you hate smokers who . . .
. . . insist upon smoking in crowded places!

Don't you hate smokers who . . .
. . . stuff auto ashtrays so full they're impossible to remove!

Don't you hate smokers who . . .
. . . never remember where they leave burning cigarettes!

Don't you hate smokers who . . .
. . . wait forever before flicking their ashes!

Don't you hate smokers who . . .
. . . are constantly spitting out bits of tobacco!

Don't you hate smokers who . . .
. . . sneak smokes in "No Smoking" areas!

Don't you hate smokers who . . .
. . . . are dentists or doctors and work on you between puffs!

Don't you hate smokers who . . .
. . . always say, "It's good for the rug!"

Don't you hate smokers who . . .
. . . tap their pipes on any handy surface to clean them!

Don't you hate smokers who . . .
. . . keep grinding out a butt till it's time to light another!

ONE DAY AT THE OCEAN

THE
LIGHTER
SIDE OF...

TRANS-
PORTATION

ARTIST & WRITER: DAVE BERG

Just watch those lovely Stewardesses . . . the way they bring the drinks, and serve the food, and clean up afterwards! They're fantastic!

I'll say! Boy, would I like to have something like that at home!!

Fine! I'll be glad to arrange it!

I've been ASKING you for a maid for years!!

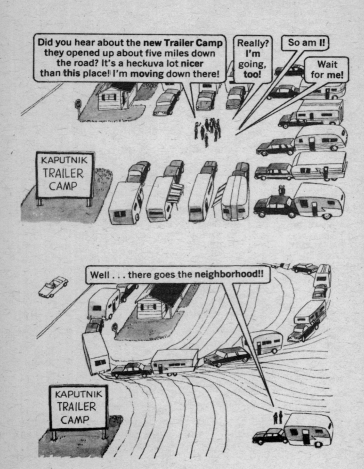

HOLD IT!!

What are you, **crazy** or something? Is it really **worth** it, running for a train like that? You could get a **heart attack** . . . or slip under the **wheels!** Everything with you guys in business is rush—rush—**RUSH!!**

You're right—puff-puff! My **doctor** told me the **same thing** —puff-puff! He said all this rushing around was **ruining my health**—puff—and I'd better take me a **nice long vacation!**

So what were you **rushing** for?

If I missed this **train**, I would've missed my plane to **Miami Beach!**

You

Never Really

YOU NEVER REALLY GET USED TO . . .

. . . the chalk breaking and your
fingernails scraping across the blackboard!

GET USED TO...

YOU NEVER REALLY GET USED TO ...

... seeing a police car in the rear-view mirror, even when you know you aren't doing anything wrong!

ARTIST:
PAUL COKER, JR.

WRITER:
TOM KOCH

YOU NEVER REALLY GET USED TO...

... having your radio-alarm go off while
an Ethel Merman record is playing!

YOU NEVER REALLY GET USED TO...

... having a dog watch
you get undressed!

YOU NEVER REALLY GET USED TO...

...waiting for the doctor to tell you how your medical tests and x-rays came out!

YOU NEVER REALLY GET USED TO...

...the fact that foreigners can't be made to understand English better if you yell at them!

YOU NEVER REALLY GET USED TO...

... those new plumbing fixtures that control the water temperature with just one faucet!

YOU NEVER REALLY GET USED TO...

... throwing away junk mail that says you *may* have already won $100,000!

YOU NEVER REALLY GET USED TO...

... trying to carry on a casual conversation with a nun!

YOU NEVER REALLY GET USED TO...

... watching an airline stewardess demonstrate how to use the emergency oxygen equipment!

. . . discovering that first tiny
scratch on your brand new car!

. . . being informed that "the
Dentist is ready for you, now!"

YOU NEVER REALLY GET USED TO...

... the scrunchie sound that big black
bugs make when you step on them!

YOU NEVER REALLY GET USED TO...

... the regular weekly test of your
neighborhood air raid siren!

YOU NEVER REALLY GET USED TO . . .

. . . public rest room booths that
cannot be locked from the inside!

ONE AFTERNOON AT THE BEACH

FLOOT THWIP THOP KLOP

FLAK FLOK SWIT GLAP

COFFEE, TEA AND MILKED DEPT.

Hey, gang! Getting sick of all those "Now" films with little or no *story-line?*
Pictures like "Midnight Cowboy", "Easy Rider", "Alice's Restaurant", "MASH",
etc. Do you sometimes wish that somebody would bring back *stories* in motion
pictures like they had in the *old* days? Well, somebody *has!* Boy, **HAVE** they!
They've come up with a movie that not only has a *plot*, but enough left over
for 37 more "Now" pictures! We're referring, of course, to MAD's nomination
for an Academy Award "Oscar"...namely a 1946 Academy Award "Oscar"...

AIRPLOT

ARTIST: MORT DRUCKER   WRITER: LARRY SIEGEL

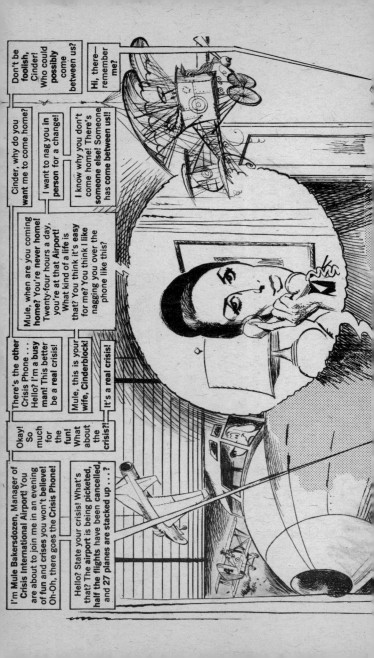

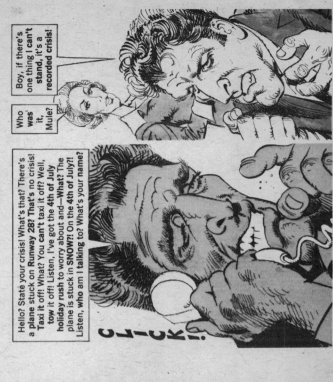

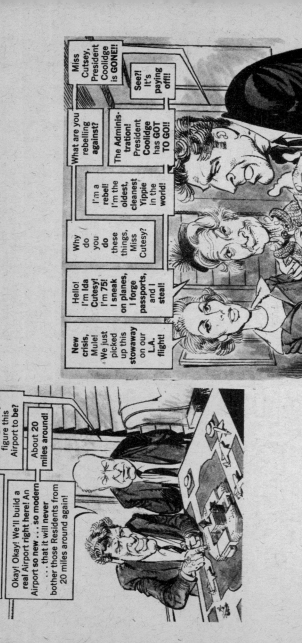

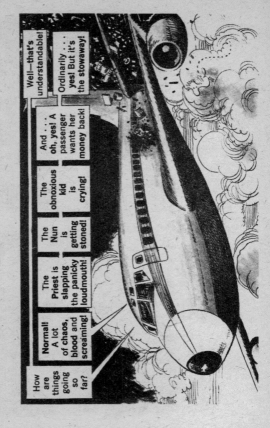

How is she, Doc? Give it to me straight!
I'm afraid she's got Mantovani's "Begin The Beguine"!
Idiot! That's not your stethoscope! You're using a Stereo Head Set!!
Flight 73 to Crisis! We have a hole in our side, two engines gone, we're out of fuel, and we have injured passengers aboard! Requesting permission to land immediately! This is an EMERGENCY!!
Sorry, guys, but you'll have to wait your turn! You call that an "Emergency"?! Around here, that's just a COFFEE BREAK!!
Listen, we're coming in!
Are you crazy?! My controllers are on strike, my electricians just walked out, there are no field lights, and we're buried under 15 feet of snow! Suggest you land in Philadelphia!
Philadelphia?! Man, are you kidding?! If we make it, there's nothing to do in Philadelphia! We're coming in!

What those poor people have been through! A mid-air bombing, a wrecked plane, a harrowing flight, and a miraculous landing . . . cheating death! Well, Mule—that's it! I guess the crises are over for tonight!

Oh, yeah?! Let's get back to my office!

What happened, Father!? We had so much more drama we could've wrung out of this situation . . . so much more blood, and screaming, and carrying on by passengers! I was planning an exciting belly-landing! Maybe even flipping over! But it ended so fast—so easy! How do you explain it?

You may find this hard to believe, my son . . . but God got BORED!

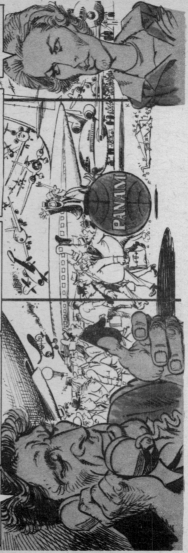